A Cat for All Seasons
Day Book

A CAT FOR ALL SEASONS
DAY BOOK

ILLUSTRATED BY ISABELLE BRENT

HARRY N. ABRAMS, INC., PUBLISHERS, NEW YORK

ISBN 0–8109–3176–1

Copyright © Isabelle Brent 1991

First published in 1991 by
Pavilion Productions Ltd., London
A division of Pavilion Books Ltd.

Published in 1992 by Harry N. Abrams, Incorporated,
New York
A Times Mirror Company

Designed by Ron Pickless

Printed and bound in Italy by L.E.G.O.

INTRODUCTION

My paintings of cats are born of a love and fascination for medieval manuscripts, be they European, Persian, Russian, or Chinese. My subjects are depicted against a variety of backgrounds, both naturalistic and imaginary, often with birds and animals concealed in the decorative borders. Sometimes the backgrounds combine with the border, and occasionally the cat may extend out of the picture on one side. There is no set formula, but always I try to paint in such a way that there is something new to be seen or found, so that each picture is fresh and interesting. Color and gold leaf are very important – whatever the dominant color, a certain blue is always apparent.

I enjoy painting cats, especially humble house cats, for they have a grace and poise, great style and finesse that few other animals possess so effortlessly. Many other artists have celebrated the cat, but in *A Cat For All Seasons,* you will find my own contribution to the many pieces dedicated to the feline. And finally, each cat is modeled on a real animal belonging either to me or to one of my numerous cat-loving friends.

Isabelle Brent

January

1

2

3

4

5

6

7

JANUARY _____

8 _____

9 _____

10 _____

11 _____

12 _____

13 _____

14 _____

15

16

17

18

19

20

21

JANUARY

22

23

24

25

26

27

28

29 _____

30 _____

31 _____

1 _____

2 _____

3 _____

4 _____

FEBRUARY _____

5 _____

6 _____

7 _____

8 _____

9 _____

10 _____

11 _____

February

12

13

14

15

16

17

18

FEBRUARY _____

19 _____

20 _____

21 _____

22 _____

23 _____

24 _____

25 _____

26 _____

27 _____

28 _____

29 _____

1 _____

2 _____

3 _____

MARCH _____

4 _____

5 _____

6 _____

7 _____

8 _____

9 _____

10 _____

MARCH _____

11 _____

12 _____

13 _____

14 _____

15 _____

16 _____

17 _____

March

18

19

20

21

22

23

24

MARCH _____

25 _____

26 _____

27 _____

28 _____

29 _____

30 _____

31 _____

APRIL _____

1 _____

2 _____

3 _____

4 _____

5 _____

6 _____

7 _____

APRIL _____

8 _____

9 _____

10 _____

11 _____

12 _____

13 _____

14 _____

APRIL

15

16

17

18

19

20

21

APRIL _____

22 _____

23 _____

24 _____

25 _____

26 _____

27 _____

28 _____

APRIL/MAY _____

29 _____

30 _____

1 _____

2 _____

3 _____

4 _____

5 _____

MAY _____

6 _____

7 _____

8 _____

9 _____

10 _____

11 _____

12 _____

MAY _____

13 _____

14 _____

15 _____

16 _____

17 _____

18 _____

19 _____

MAY _____

20 _____

21 _____

22 _____

23 _____

24 _____

25 _____

26 _____

MAY/JUNE _____

27 _____

28 _____

29 _____

30 _____

31 _____

1 _____

2 _____

June _____

3 _____

4 _____

5 _____

6 _____

7 _____

8 _____

9 _____

JUNE _____

10 _____

11 _____

12 _____

13 _____

14 _____

15 _____

16 _____

JUNE _____

17 _____

18 _____

19 _____

20 _____

21 _____

22 _____

23 _____

JUNE _____

24 _____

25 _____

26 _____

27 _____

28 _____

29 _____

30 _____

JULY _____

1 _____

2 _____

3 _____

4 _____

5 _____

6 _____

7 _____

July _____

8 _____

9 _____

10 _____

11 _____

12 _____

13 _____

14 _____

15 _____

16 _____

17 _____

18 _____

19 _____

20 _____

21 _____

JULY _____

22 _____

23 _____

24 _____

25 _____

26 _____

27 _____

28 _____

JULY/AUGUST _____

29 _____

30 _____

31 _____

1 _____

2 _____

3 _____

4 _____

AUGUST _____

5 _____

6 _____

7 _____

8 _____

9 _____

10 _____

11 _____

AUGUST _____

12 _____

13 _____

14 _____

15 _____

16 _____

17 _____

18 _____

AUGUST _____

19 _____

20 _____

21 _____

22 _____

23 _____

24 _____

25 _____

26 _____

27 _____

28 _____

29 _____

30 _____

31 _____

1 _____

2 _____

3 _____

4 _____

5 _____

6 _____

7 _____

8 _____

9

10

11

12

13

14

15

September

16 _____

17 _____

18 _____

19 _____

20 _____

21 _____

22 _____

September

23

24

25

26

27

28

29

30 _____

1 _____

2 _____

3 _____

4 _____

5 _____

6 _____

OCTOBER _____

7 _____

8 _____

9 _____

10 _____

11 _____

12 _____

13 _____

OCTOBER _____

14 _____

15 _____

16 _____

17 _____

18 _____

19 _____

20 _____

OCTOBER _____

21 _____

22 _____

23 _____

24 _____

25 _____

26 _____

27 _____

28

29

30

31

1

2

3

November

4 _____

5 _____

6 _____

7 _____

8 _____

9 _____

10 _____

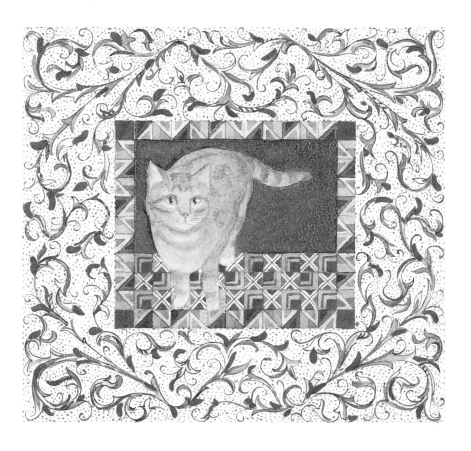

November

11

12

13

14

15

16

17

NOVEMBER _____

18 _____

19 _____

20 _____

21 _____

22 _____

23 _____

24 _____

25 _____

26 _____

27 _____

28 _____

29 _____

30 _____

1 _____

December

2

3

4

5

6

7

8

9 _____

10 _____

11 _____

12 _____

13 _____

14 _____

15 _____

December

16

17

18

19

20

21

22

DECEMBER _____

23 _____

24 _____

25 _____

26 _____

27 _____

28 _____

29 _____

DECEMBER

30

31